Y0-CLV-908

BRAHMS

THE INTERNATIONAL LIBRARY OF MUSIC

Including many of the compositions edited by
IGNACE J. PADEREWSKI
Reprinted from the original plates of
his Century Library of Music

Piano Series

ADVISORY BOARD ON MUSICAL PUBLICATIONS

RUDOLPH GANZ
President, Chicago Musical College

EDWIN HUGHES
Virtuoso and Teacher

THOMAS TAPPER, LITT.D.
New York Institute of Musical Art

J. LAWRENCE ERB
Connecticut College for Women

KATE S. CHITTENDEN
Dean of Music, Vassar College

A. MADELEY RICHARDSON, Mus. Doc. Oxon.
Julliard School of Music

CHARLES DENNÉE
New England Conservatory of Music

G. ACKELEY BROWER
Cadek Conservatory of Music

GEORGE FOLSOM GRANBERRY
Granberry School of Music

LEO C. MILLER
Miller Music Studios

F. CAMPBELL-WATSON, M.A.
Managing Editor

Associate and Contributing Editors for Musical Publications

FRANZ C. BORNSCHEIN AUGUST FRAEMCKE GUSTAV L. BECKER
HENRY HOLDEN HUSS FELIX BOROWSKI
ARTHUR FOOTE SIDNEY SILBER

VOLUME VII

PIANOFORTE COMPOSITIONS

THE UNIVERSITY SOCIETY
INCORPORATED
NEW YORK

Copyright, 1934 by
THE UNIVERSITY SOCIETY
INCORPORATED

In addition to a wealth of new material, this new edition of The International Library of Music combines the best features of its highly successful predecessors; namely:

Famous Songs and Those Who Made Them ....Copyright 1896
The World's Best Music ....Copyright 1897
Paderewski—Century Library of Music ....Copyright 1900
Modern Music and Musicians ....Copyright 1912
La Mejor Musica del Mundo ....Copyright 1917
The University Course of Music Study ....Copyright 1920
The International Library of Music ....Copyright 1925
A Melhor Musica do Mundo ....Copyright 1930

MANUFACTURED IN THE U. S. A.

TABLE OF CONTENTS

VOLUME SEVEN

		PAGE
In Crimea	M. Moussorgsky	1825
Valse, Op. 36, No. 7	Anton Arensky	1830
Nocturne, Op. 48, No. 1	F. Chopin	1838
Barcarolle, *A minor*	Anton Rubinstein	1844
If I Were a Bird, Op. 2, No. 6	Adolf Henselt	1852
Prelude and Fugue, Op. 35, No. 1	F. Mendelssohn	1857
On Wings of Song	Mendelssohn-Liszt	1870
March, Op. 24, No. 2	Edward MacDowell	1876
Melodie	S. Rachmaninoff	1881
Nocturne, Op. 15, No. 1	F. Chopin	1886
Serenade Levantine, Op. 25. No. 3	A. Alpheraky	1892
España	Emanuel Chabrier	1896
Polichinelle	S. Rachmaninoff	1906
Rhapsodie, Op. 79, No. 1	Johannes Brahms	1914
Rhapsodie, Op. 79. No. 2	Johannes Brahms	1924
Ballade	Claude Debussy	1932
The Maiden's Wish (Chant Polonais)	Chopin-Liszt	1941
My Joys (Chant Polonais)	Chopin-Liszt	1948
Valse, Op. 10, No. 2	S. Rachmaninoff	1954
Valse. Op. 64, No. 3	F. Chopin	1963
Aufschwung. Op. 12, No. 2	Robert Schumann	1970
Träumeswirren, Op. 12. No. 7	Robert Schumann	1976
Caprice a la Scarlatti, Op. 14, No. 3	I. J Paderewski	1982
Suite, *D minor*	G. F. Handel	1987
Nocturne, Op. 62, No. 1	F. Chopin	2004
Des Abends, Op. 12, No. 1	Robert Schumann	2010
Barcarolle, Op. 50, No. 3	Anton Rubinstein	2014
Momento Capriccioso, Op. 12	Carl M. von Weber	2018
By Moonlight, Op. 139, No. 3	Franz Bendel	2024
Gavotte and Musette, from Suite in *D minor,* Op. 1, No. 4	Eugen d'Albert	2034
La Fileuse, Op. 157, No. 2	Joachim Raff	2038
Barcarolle, Op. 10, No. 3	S. Rachmaninoff	2045
Impromptu, Op. 29	F. Chopin	2054
Pavane pour une enfant defunte	Maurice Ravel	2061
Bigarrure, Op. 20, No. 1	Anton Arensky	2066
March, Op. 39, No. 1	Alexis Hollaender	2072
Basso Ostinato, Op. 5	Anton Arensky	2078
Capriccio, Op. 76, No. 2	Johannes Brahms	2082
Pres de la Mer, Op. 52, No. 5	Anton Arensky	2088
Reverie	Claude Debussy	2092
Nocturne, Op. 15, No. 2	F. Chopin	2096
Prelude and Fugue, W.T.C., No. 1	J. S. Bach	2100
Polonaise, Op. 40, No. 2	F. Chopin	2105
Arabeske, Op. 18	Robert Schumann	2112
Etude, Op. 23, No. 2	Anton Rubinstein	2120

IN CRIMEA
IMPRESSIONS DE VOYAGE EN CRIMÉE

MODESTE MOUSSORGSKY

sfp
sf
sfp
cresc.
p
pp

poco rit.
a tempo
p
cresc.
Energico
f
sf

a tempo
p
poco rit.
mf
p tranquillo
sf
f
poco allargando
meno mosso e più allargando
dim.
pp rall.

Largo
pp
pp
pp
pp
p
pp
pp
pp
rit.
ppp

VALSE
E-FLAT MAJOR

Edited by
August Fraemcke

ANTON ARENSKY
Op. 36, Nº 7.

mf
p
Ped.
*

rit.
a tempo
mf
p

ff
ff
Ped.
p
rit.

a tempo
mf
p
mf

dim.
p
dim.
pp
ritard.
Tempo I
ppp
ppp
accel.
pppp

1838

NOCTURNE

C MINOR

From the CENTURY LIBRARY *of* MUSIC
Edited by Ignace J. Paderewski

CHOPIN
Op. 48, Nº 1

ten.
Poco più lento
ten.
T.S.P.
sotto voce ed arpeggiando
sempre p
pp
cresc.

legato
legato
p
p cre - scen - do
p cre - scen - do
p cre - scen - do
p cre - scen - do
p cre - scen - do
p cre - scen - do
p cre - scen - do
ff
riten
sempre ff
Ped.
T.S.P

riten.
fz
p acceler.
T.S.P.
Doppio movimento
pp agitato e legato
legato il basso
segue
cresc.

Ped. Ped. Ped. Ped. Ped. * Ped. *

Ped. Ped. Ped. Ped.

Ped. Ped. Ped. Ped. * Ped. Ped. Ped. *

fz

Ped. * Ped. * Ped. * Ped. *

cre - - scen - - do

Ped. * Ped. Ped. * Ped. Ped. * Ped. *

ten.
ten.
f
ff
riten.
dim. e rall.
pp

BARCAROLLE

A MINOR

From the CENTURY LIBRARY *of* MUSIC
Edited by Ignace J. Paderewski

RUBINSTEIN

dim.
ad lib.
mf
Ped.
T.S.P.
tr
p
legg

L.H.
cresc.
f
p espressivo
pp
Ped.

animato
l.h.
cresc.
string.
leggiero
rit.
a tempo, leggiero
p
T.S.P.

string.
rit.
a tempo, sempre leggiero
sf
p
T. S P.
legato
mf
cresc.
f

string.
ad lib.
T.S.P.
a tempo
legg.
L.H.

con espressione
mf
stacc.
mf

Allegro
Ped.
f
string. poco staccato
p
ritard.
Tempo I.
p
pp leggiero

SI OISEAU J'ÉTAIS
IF I WERE A BIRD
"Si oiseau j'étais, À toi je volerais!"

From the CENTURY LIBRARY *of* MUSIC
Edited by Ignace J. Paderewski

A. HENSELT
Op. 2, No. 6

sopra
Ped.
pp
con espressione
poco riten.
a tempo
sopra
cresc. poco a poco
f

f
Ped.
più cresc.
ff
ritenuto
dim.
pp
a tempo

fz
p
f
dim. e rall.
a tempo
pp
una corda
poco rit.
a tempo
tre corde

poco riten.

pp

Ped. ※ Ped. ※ Ped. ※ Ped. ※

cresc. con anima

Ped. ※ Ped. ※ Ped. ※ Ped. ※

dimin. e dolce

cresc. con calore

Ped. ※ Ped. ※ Ped. ※ Ped. ※ Ped. ※

dimin.

f

Ped. ※ Ped. ※ Ped. ※ Ped. ※ Ped. ※

ral - len - tan - do

Lento

morendo

f p

Ped. ※ Ped. ※ Ped. ※ Ped. ※ Ped. ※ Ped. ※ Ped. ※

PRELUDE AND FUGUE

From the CENTURY LIBRARY *of* MUSIC
Edited by Ignace J. Paderewski

E MINOR

F. MENDELSSOHN
Op. 35, No. 1

PRELUDE
Allegro molto

sf
sf
l.h.
R. H.
R.H.
pp
f
r.h.
Ped.

p
dim.
pp
l.h.
cresc.
f
R.H.
sf
r.h.

Ped.
sf
R. H.
r. h.
cresc.
f
dim.
p
dim.
pp
leggiero

FUGUE

f
p
cresc.
ff
T.S.P.

R.H.
l.h.
R.H.

ff
Ped.
L.H.
f

p
sf
meno forte

f
Ped.
poco a poco cresc.

f
ff
T.S.P.

Ped.
ff
sf

sf
sf
simile
sempre ff
simile
ff
sf
sf
sf

ON WINGS OF SONG

AUF FLÜGELN DES GESANGES

From the CENTURY LIBRARY *of* MUSIC
Edited by Ignace J. Paderewski

MENDELSSOHN-LISZT

sempre legato
p
dim.
p
p poco rit.
Ped.

sfz
dim.
pp
sempre legato e tranquillo

un poco agitato

cre - - - scen - - - - do

rit.

cre - - - scen - - - do
dimin.
dolce
dolce
legato
legato
Ped.

cresc.
appassionato
poco rall. smorz.
decresc. e legato
più dimin.
pp
pp

MARCH

E. A. MACDOWELL
Op. 24, No. 2

fff
ten.
p
pp
pp
ff
quasi trombe
cresc.
p dolce
cresc.
mf
f

ff
mf
dolce
simile
ff
pesante
mf
p
pp
dim.

ppp
poco cresc.
f marc.
ten.
ten.
ten.
ten.
ten.
f
ff pesante
8
fff

8
fff grandioso
marcatiss.
sempre pesante
ten.
fz
pp
dim.
ten.
p
pp
pp
ppp
perdendosi

MELODIE

SERGEI RACHMANINOFF
Op. 10, No. 4

mf
p
p
mf
pp
ppp
mf
f
dimin.
p
f
p
rit.

pp
ppp
Allegro moderato
mf
f
p
f
p
mf
pp
ppp

mf
f
p
mf
f
p
p
pp
rit.
3
Allegretto
mf
mf
mf

cresc.
f
p
pp
Moderato (♪ = ♩)
mf
ppp
8
pp
rit. e dim.

NOCTURNE
F MAJOR

From the CENTURY LIBRARY *of* MUSIC
Edited by Ignace J. Paderewski

CHOPIN
Op. 15, Nº 1

Andante cantabile

Ped.
dolciss
smorz.
Con fuoco.(♩=84.)
f

rfz
cresc.
ff
dim.
fz
pp e poco riten.
dim.
T.S.P.
a tempo
dim.
cresc.

Con fuoco
f
Ped.
fz
cre - scen - do
sempre legato
pfz
pp

dim.
rall. e calando
Tempo I.
sotto voce
p
poco cresc. e riten.
dolciss.

dolciss.
pp
dim.
rall.
smorz.
T.S.P.

SERENADE LEVANTINE
Edited by
Vernon Spencer
A. ALPHÉRAKY
Op. 25, No. 3
Moderato (♩= 60)
mf
mp
cantando
p
simile
più f
sf
p
ritenuto
a tempo
p legatissimo e dolce

cresc. molto
ff legato
TSP and Damper Ped. as well
TSP
TSP
TSP
TSP
TSP
dim.
p
TSP
p
leggiero
cresc. assai

8
f
TSP
pp
cresc. poco a poco
ff
p

Con moto, quasi cadenza
p cresc.
simile
f dim.
senza Ped.
senza Ped.
rit. poco a poco
p a tempo
dim.
l. h.
l. h.
l. h.
l. h.
senza Ped.
pp

ESPANA

RHAPSODIE

EMMANUEL CHABRIER
Arranged by Irénée Bergé

ff
ff
sf
sf
ff
sf
mf

ff
sf
ff
sf
dim.
p
f marcato
p
ff

dolce espress.
sf
p
sf
ff appassionato

molto cresc.
ff
ff
sf
ff
p
f

8
espress.
p
f
f

ff
ff
mf leggierissimo
cresc.
mf cantabile

cresc.
pp leggierissimo

p
cresc.
f
cresc.
ff
ff
ff
8

POLICHINELLE

PUNCHINELLO

SERGEI RACHMANINOFF
Op. 3, No. 4

Allegro vivace

p
ff
sfff
sfff
8
8
8

p
ff
ff
p
ff
sfff

sfff

Agitato

f

dim. *p*

p
pp
f
dim.
p
p
pp

f
sfff
sfff
l.h.
sfff
sfff
sfff
sfff
sfff
ppp
p

ff
f
fff
f
fff
8

f
ff
sfff
fff

1914

RHAPSODIE
B MINOR

Edited by
Rudolph Ganz

JOHANNES BRAHMS
Op. 79, Nº 1.

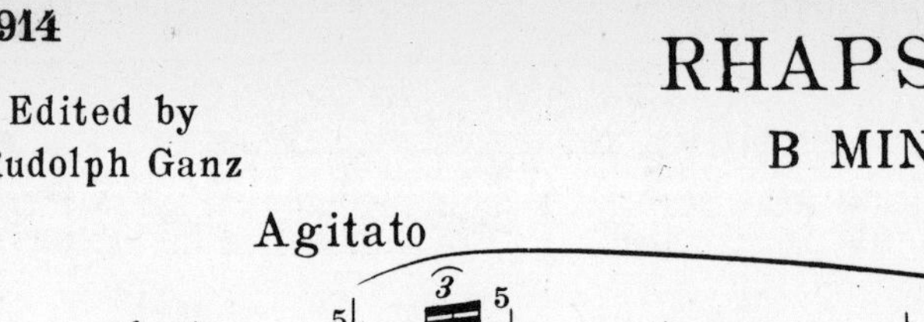

rubato
f
p
pp
Ped.
poco rit.
f a tempo
cresc.
f energico
8

simile
f
rfz
p subito
sempre cresc.
f
ff marcatissimo
Ped.
Ped.
f
ff
fz
Ped.
TSP

f
cresc.
f
p
sostenuto
più f
Ped.
Stretto
8
sf
Pesante
f
dim.
rit.

p molto dol. espress.
a tempo
1.
2.
cresc.
dim.
p
cresc.
con calore
dim.
dol.

1.
2.
p
dim.
poco rit.
pp
Ped.
* Ped.
f a tempo
*
f
cresc.
f
l. h.
fp

sostenuto sempre
p
p
pp
a tempo
poco rit.
f a tempo

p
cresc.
f
8
f
rfz
cresc. sempre
8

ff
fz
f
cresc.
f
più f

sf
segue
fp
p
leggiero
poco a poco sempre rit. e dim.
r. h.
r. h.
pp
ppp
Ped.

RHAPSODIE

G MINOR, No. II.

Edited by
Sidney Silber

JOHANNES BRAHMS
Op. 79, No. 2.

più agitato
cresc.
riten.
a tempo
p misterioso
due corde
tre corde
crescendo
marcato
rit.
a tempo
l.h.

l.h.
p espressivo
ritard.
p
a tempo
p
rit.

a tempo
due corde
r.h.
l.h.
rit.
p
a tempo
sempre due corde
misterioso
tre corde
ff
p
poco rit.
a tempo
ff
p
dim.

l.h.
l.h.
rit.
ppp
sotto voce
a tempo
due corde
(r.h.)
poco rit.
a tempo
tre corde

ff
p
(l.h.)
pp
due corde
accel.
dim.
ritenuto
lunga
a tempo
f
Ped.
tre corde
l.h.
rit.
a tempo
l.h.
rit.
a tempo
f
Ped.

f
molto rit.
mp a tempo
(senza Ped.)
cresc.
f
riten.
p a tempo
due corde

Grandioso
f
cresc.
tre corde
marcato
ff pesante
ff
p dim.
quasi rit.
T.S.P.
pp
smorzando
ppp
ff

BALLADE

Edited by
Rudolph Ganz

CLAUDE DEBUSSY

Copyright MCMXIX, by The University Society, Inc.

cresc. un poco
espressivo
mf
poco marcato
mp
espress.
p
cresc. un poco
poco rit.
mf
a tempo
p
pp

cresc.
dim.
pp
più sonore
cresc. un poco
simile
Con larghezza
mf cresc.
f molto cresc.
con calore
meno f
dim.
poco rit.
a tempo
p
p

cresc.
p
simile
rit.
a tempo
pp
Un poco più mosso
p
rit.
Tempo I.
pp tranquillo
pp
p
pp

p
cresc.
poco accel.
rit. e dim.
pp
pp
dolce marcato
pp animando poco a poco
p ben portando ed espressivo
p
pp
simile

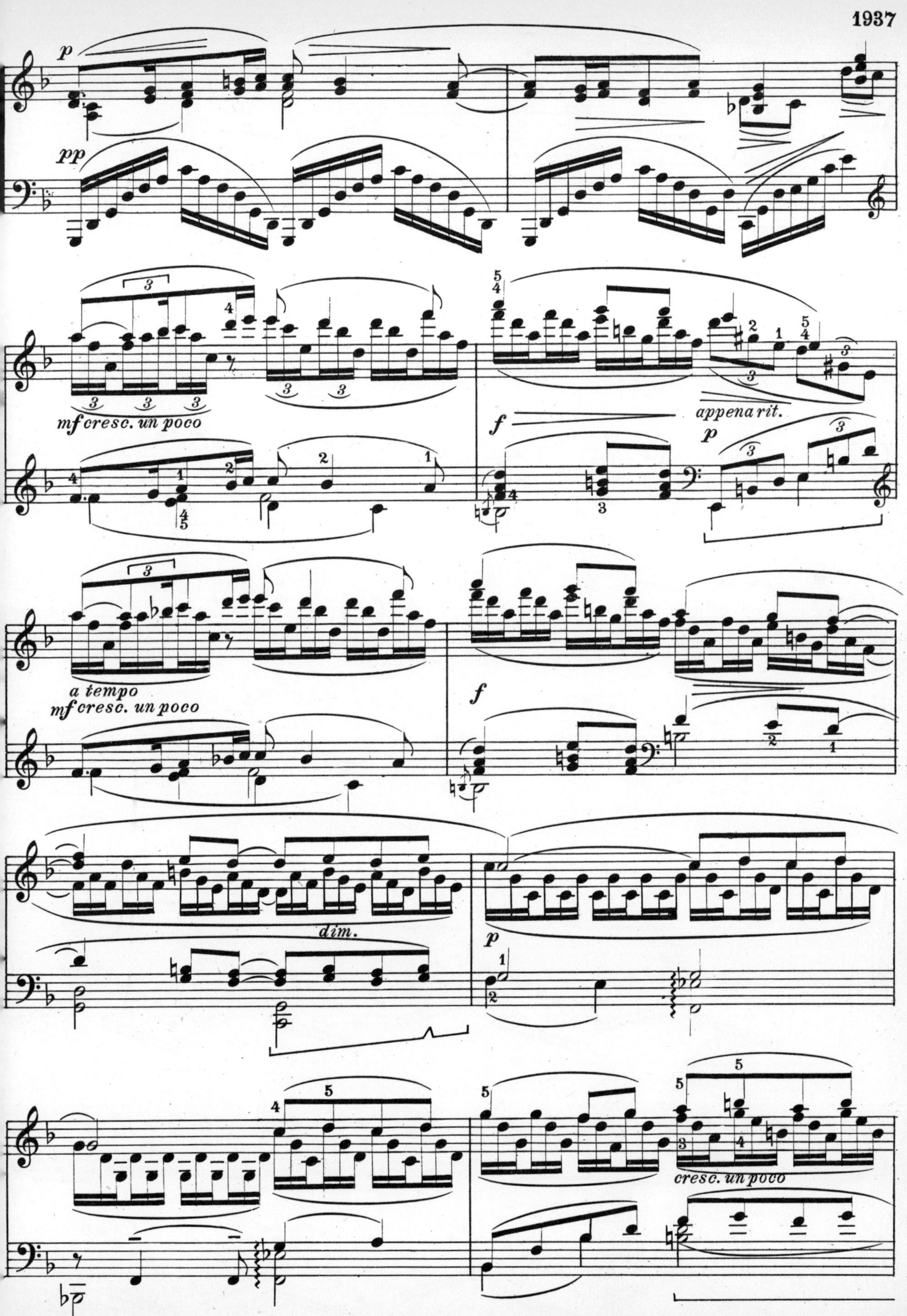
p
pp
mf cresc. un poco
f
appena rit.
p
a tempo
mf cresc. un poco
f
dim.
p
cresc. un poco

molto calmato
rit.
r.h.
p
a tempo
r.h.
pp
sempre
armonioso
simile
cresc. poco a poco

Con larghezza

cresc. molto

f

ff

poco dim.

f

dim.

p espressivo

rit.

a tempo

pp

pp

Tempo I.
molto rit.
ppp
pp
simile
l.h.
pp
p
mp
r.h.
pp poco ritenuto
ten.
rall.
ppp

THE MAIDEN'S WISH

CHANT POLONAIS

(Transcription)

From the CENTURY LIBRARY *of* MUSIC
Edited by Ignace J. Paderewski

CHOPIN-LISZT

Un poco meno allegro
dolce espress.
senza Pedale
espress.
una corda
tre corde
Tempo I.

Variante I.
Un poco meno Allegro
p
dolce con grazia
sempre legato
poco rall.
rinforz.
T.S.P.
dim.
smorz.

Variante II.

8
Ped.

Variante III.

Vivace
p
una corda
pp
più dim.
perdendo
ppp

MY JOYS
CHANT POLONAIS
(Transcription)

From the CENTURY LIBRARY *of* MUSIC
Edited by Ignace J. Paderewski

CHOPIN - LISZT

rinforz.
pp
agitato
rit.
agitato
più appassionato
dim.
pp

3/4 rit
smorz.
pp
T.S.P.
leggiero
rinforz.
p
rinforz.
p
rinforz.
T.S.P.
tr
leggiero

accelerando
p
segue
più accelerando e string. molto
ff con somma passione
marcato
sempre ff

Ped.
Ped.
sf
2/4
3/4

dolce e semplice
rit.
pp
perdendosi

VALSE

A MAJOR

Edited by
August Fraemcke

SERGE RACHMANINOFF
Op.10, № 2

Allegro assai

f
accel.
dim.
con allegria.
p
accel.

con moto
mf
cresc. ed accel.

ff
Presto
r. h.
l. h.
ff
dim.
ritard.

Allegro moderato
p
Ped.
cresc.
dim.

p
p
p
accel.

Tempo I.
mf
rit.
a tempo.
cresc.
accel.
dim.
p con allegria.
p

pp
mf
dim.
p
accel.

Presto
pp
ppp
Ped.
cresc.
f
cresc. molto
sfff
l. h.
fff

VALSE

A-flat

F. CHOPIN
Op. 64, No. 3

f
p
cresc.
f
p

cresc.
cresc.
riten.
f

p sotto voce
cresc.

poco riten.
a tempo
sostenuto
f

mf
p
cresc.
f
f

dim.
p poco a poco accel. al fine
8
cresc.
f
8
decresc.
8
cresc.

AUFSCHWUNG
SOARING

From the CENTURY LIBRARY *of* MUSIC
Edited by Ignace J. Paderewski

SCHUMAN
Op. 12, No.

p
simile
rit.
mf
simile
rh
f
sf
ff

sf
ff
f
dim. e rit.
mf a tempo
p
mf
dim.
r.h.
ritard.
sf
scherz.

sf
sf
Ped.
sf
sf
Ped.
ritard.
Ped.
mf
p
Ped.
Ped.
Ped.
Ped.
Ped.
Ped.
Ped.
Ped.

ff
sf
f
p
simile
35
45
Ped.

pp
simile
rit.
mf a tempo
simile
rit.
a tempo
f
sf
ff
f

TRAUMESWIRREN

DREAM FANCIES

SCHUMANN
Op.12, Nº 7

p
f
p
f
f
p
f
sf
sfp
sfp
*T.S.P.
p
sf
sf
rit.

legatissimo
pp
pp più lento e tranquillo
sf
f
p

Tempo I
p
mf
f
sf
sf
sf
sf
f
sf
sf
f
ff
sf
sf
p
sf
p
cres
cen

do
sf
sf p
sf
rit.
a tempo
sf
sf
sf
sf
p
sf
sf
sf
sf
sf
p
sf
sf

mf
ritard.
pp
pp
una corda

CAPRICE À LA SCARLATTI

From the CENTURY LIBRARY *of* MUSIC
Edited by Ignace J. Paderewski

I. J. PADEREWSKI
Op. 14, No. 3.

l.h.

tr

cresc.

Ped. *

Ped.

* Ped.

sf

8

8

Ped.

Ped. *

8
Ped.
Ped.
8
f
Ped.
sf
5

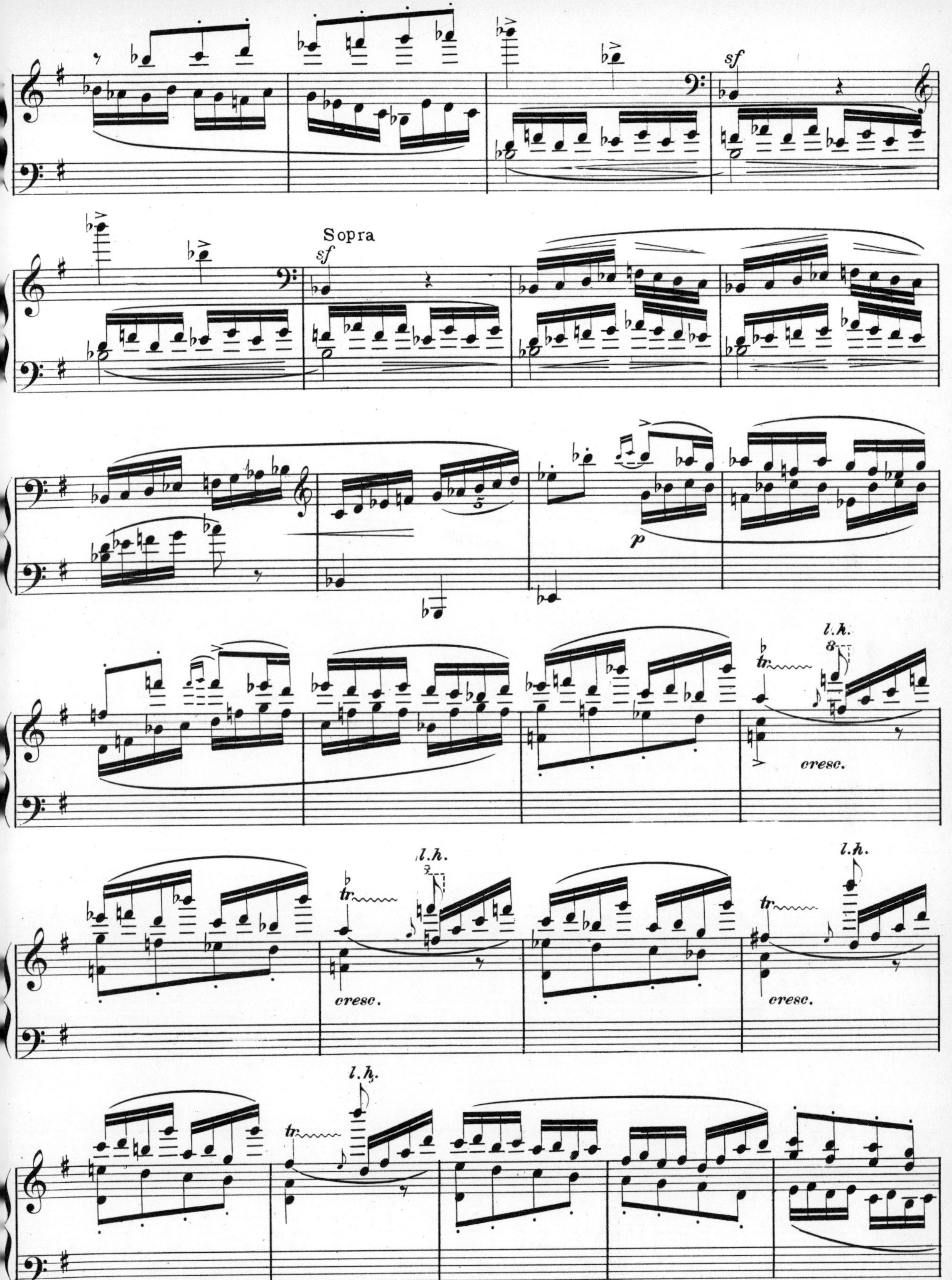
sf
Sopra
sf
p
l.h.
8
cresc.
l.h.
cresc.
l.h.
cresc.
l.h.
tr

ff
Ped.
ff
Ped.
Ped.
Ped.

SUITE

D MINOR

HÄNDEL

From the CENTURY LIBRARY *of* MUSIC
Edited by Ignace J. Paderewski

ff
rall.
sff
brillante.
Adagio
T. S. P.
FUGA
Allegro
p
mf
f
L.H.

f
Ped.
cresc.
p
Ped.
Ped.
f
cresc.
Ped.
ff
pp
mf
Ped.
f
Ped.

mf
Ped.
a tempo
poco rit.
Adagio
ff

ALLEMANDE

poco cresc.
cresc.

COURANTE

Adagio molto

sopra
sotto.
1.
2.

I.
DOUBLE
p
Ped.
mf
f
più f
II.
DOUBLE
1.
2.
sempre f

f
Ped.
III.
DOUBLE
p
mf
cresc.
dim.

IV.
DOUBLE

V.
DOUBLE

PRESTO

f
fp
f
f
rall.
ff a tempo
tr
p
f

pp legato
p
pp
p
pp
cresc.
f
dim.
p
ff
p
f
p.
mf
ff
Ped.

tr
fz
f
p
cresc.
f sost.
poco rall.
Ped.

NOCTURNE
B MAJOR

F. CHOPIN
Op. 62, №1

sempre legato
dim.
dim.
pp
f
fz
p
rall.

* The melody from which Chopin elaborated this movement may be disengaged in this form:—

after which follows a cadenza in Italian style till the second part of the theme appears as follows:—

after which the remainder of the movement consists of a new melodic motive worked out as an interlude.

dolciss.
cresc.
f
dim.
pp
cresc.
Ped.

dim.
dolce
poco più lento
poco rallent.
a tempo
Tempo I.
pp
dim.
rall.
cresc.

dim.
riten.
a tempo
p
Ped.
pp
calando

DES ABENDS
AT EVENING

SCHUMANN
Op. 12, No. 1

p
rit.

p
Ped.
Ped. Ped. Ped. Ped. simile
p

rit.
Ped.
Ped. Ped. Ped.
Ped. simile
rit.

BARCAROLLE

G MINOR

From the CENTURY LIBRARY *of* MUSIC
Edited by Ignace J. Paderewski

A. RUBINSTEIN
Op. 50, Nº 3

Moderato con moto

poco ritardando
a tempo
R.H.
T.S.P.
Ped.
L.H.
p
dim.
pp

mormorando
una corda

p
dim.
p
sempre
una corda
pp

MOMENTO CAPRICCIOSO

B-FLAT MAJOR

From the CENTURY LIBRARY *of* MUSIC
Edited by Ignace J. Paderewski

CARL MARIA von WEBER
Op. 12.

dolce
f
p
f
p
cresc.
poco rit.
ff a tempo
simile
sf
marcato
segue
ff

f
cresc.
con bravura
ff
ritard.
a tempo
p
f
p
f
p

mf cresc e poco rit.
ff a tempo
simile
una corda
tre corde.
cresc.
ff e rit.
pp
una corda
pp
cresc. molto
f
tre corde
pp
pp
una corda
cresc. molto
ff
fz
fz
pp
tre corde
cresc. molto

ff
p
mf
mp
pp
affrettando
dim. e poco rit.
tranquillo, ma in tempo
simile

pp
cresc.
f
ff
Ped.
stringendo
poco a poco rall.
f p
pp a tempo
smorzando
una corda
pp
senza rit.
ff
sffz
tre corde

BY MOONLIGHT

(From "AM GENFER SEE.")

Edited by
August Fraemcke

FRANZ BENDEL
Op. 139, No 3

lunga
espressivo
rit.
delicatissimo
pp una corda
pp
molto espress.
leggiero

molto espressivo
lungo trillo

leggiero
Meno mosso e molto cantabile
pp
poco rit.
a tempo
f

leggiero
rit.
a tempo
pp
poco rit.
a tempo.

espressivo
fz
rit.
p
Più mosso
pp

leggiero
leggiero

Meno mosso e molto cantabile
sempre una corda
ppp
poco ritard.
a tempo
poco rit.
Cadenza
leggiero e veloce
pp

poco rit.
a tempo
Più lento
rit.
grazioso

pp
poco a poco dim.
sempre ppp e molto legato
un poco rit.
morendo
ppp

GAVOTTE AND MUSETTE

(From Suite in D minor)

Edited by
August Fraemcke

EUGEN d' ALBERT
Op. 1, No. 4.

p
8va
cresc.
f
ff
8va
Fine

Musette
pp ben legato.
pp
sf
sf
pp

8va
dim.
dolciss.
molto
pp delicato
pp
dim. e poco riten.
ppp
D. C. al Fine

LA FILEUSE
ETUDE

Edited by
Bern. Boekelman

JOACHIM RAFF
Op. 157, № 2

Ped.
* Ped. simile
l.h.
l.h.
pp

poco a poco crescendo.
f
p
rinfz.
cre
scen
do
f
rinforzando ed incalzando.
Ped.
Ped.
simile

8
Ped.
tranquillo e aolcemente.
f
p
Ped.
Ped.
Ped.
Ped.
l.h.
l.h.
l.h.

poco f
f
Ped.
dolcissimo.
pp
Ped.
simile

Ped.
Ped.
simile
Ped.

f
p
ten.
p
f
p
p
senza Ped.
8
8
pp
rit.
Ped.
*

Edited by
August Fraemcke

BARCAROLLE

SERGE RACHMANINOFF
Op. 10, Nº 3

Moderato

pp
p
pp
Con moto
ppp leggiero

p
dim.
f
pp
poco rit.
ppp
a tempo
sost.

f
f
ppp
sost.

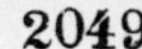

Presto

r.h. *pppp* l.h.

Ped. ✻ Ped.

ppp

✻ Ped. ✻ Ped.

Ped. ✻ Ped. ✻ Ped. *dim.* ✻ Ped.

Allegro moderato

pp *ppp* *mf*

✻ Ped. ✻

sost. Ped. ✻

sost. Ped. ✻

sost.
Ped.
cresc.
f
mf
pp

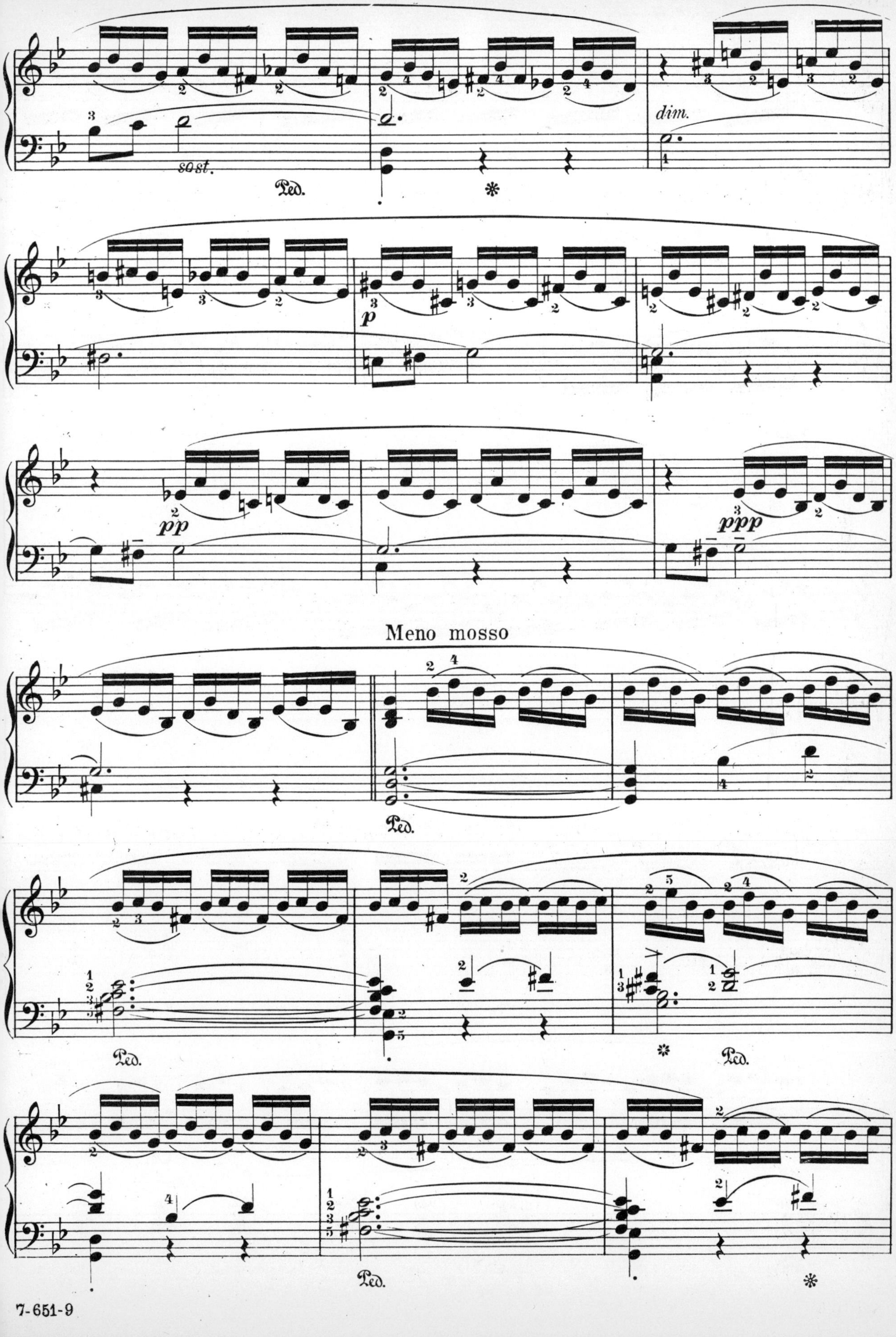

sost.
Ped.
dim.
p
pp
ppp
Meno mosso
Ped.

Ped.
Con moto
ppp
mf
f

ppp
Ped.
dim.
r.h.
pppp
l.h.
8
pp

IMPROMPTU

A-FLAT MAJOR

Edited by
Donald M. Swarthout

CHOPIN
Op. 29

dim.
p
cresc.
f
poco rit.
accel. poco a poco
p
smorzando
a tempo

p
f
r.h.
l.h.
f sostenuto
p ritenuto
ten.
f
p

f
p
f cresc.
sf
ff
mezza voce
dolcissimo
a tutta voce
mezza voce
f
cresc.
sfz
a tutta voce

8
f
17
rit.
p a tempo
legato

dim.

p

cresc.

f

poco rit.

accel. poco a poco

dim. sempre

p

smorzando
a tempo
p
sotto voce
pp
calando
pp

PAVANE
(POUR UNE ENFANT DÉFUNTE)

Edited by
Rudolph Ganz

MAURICE RAVEL

Tempo I.
come da lontano
pp
mf
ben sostenuto
pp
una corda
pp
cresc.
l.h.
Poco più lento
mf
f
tre corde

Tempo I.
p
simile
mf
poco stentando
dim.
rapido
p
a tempo
Largo
Tempo I.
pp
un poco rit.
ff
sost.
pp
subito dolcissimo
e ben sostenuto
sopra
pp

sfz
ff
Tempo I.
Grave assai
molto dim.
p
pp
sopra.
p
sfz
ff
Grave assai
sfz
ff
mf
p
pp

Tempo I.

marcato e portando il canto

p

simile

mf

poco stentando

dim.

rapido

pp

a tempo

pp *rit.*

f *molto allarg.*
molto cresc.

l.h. *r.h.*

l.h.

ff

sffz

Edited by
Charles Dennée

BIGARRURE

A. ARENSKY
Op. 20, No. 1

f
pp
f
dim. e rit.
pp
a tempo
mf
p
ff
p

Agitato
p
pp
f
dim. e rit.
a tempo
dim.
rit.
pp a tempo

poco rit.
a tempo
p
pp
f
dim. e rit.
a tempo
pp
ten.
ppp
rit.

Tempo I.

rit.
pp
a tempo
mf
pp
ff
rit.
p
Più mosso
pp
pp
una corda
ppp

MARCH

Edited by
Roy Lamont Smith

ALEXIS HOLLAENDER
Op. 39, No. 1

f
sfz
sfz
sf
cresc.
ff
mf
cresc.
f

Trio

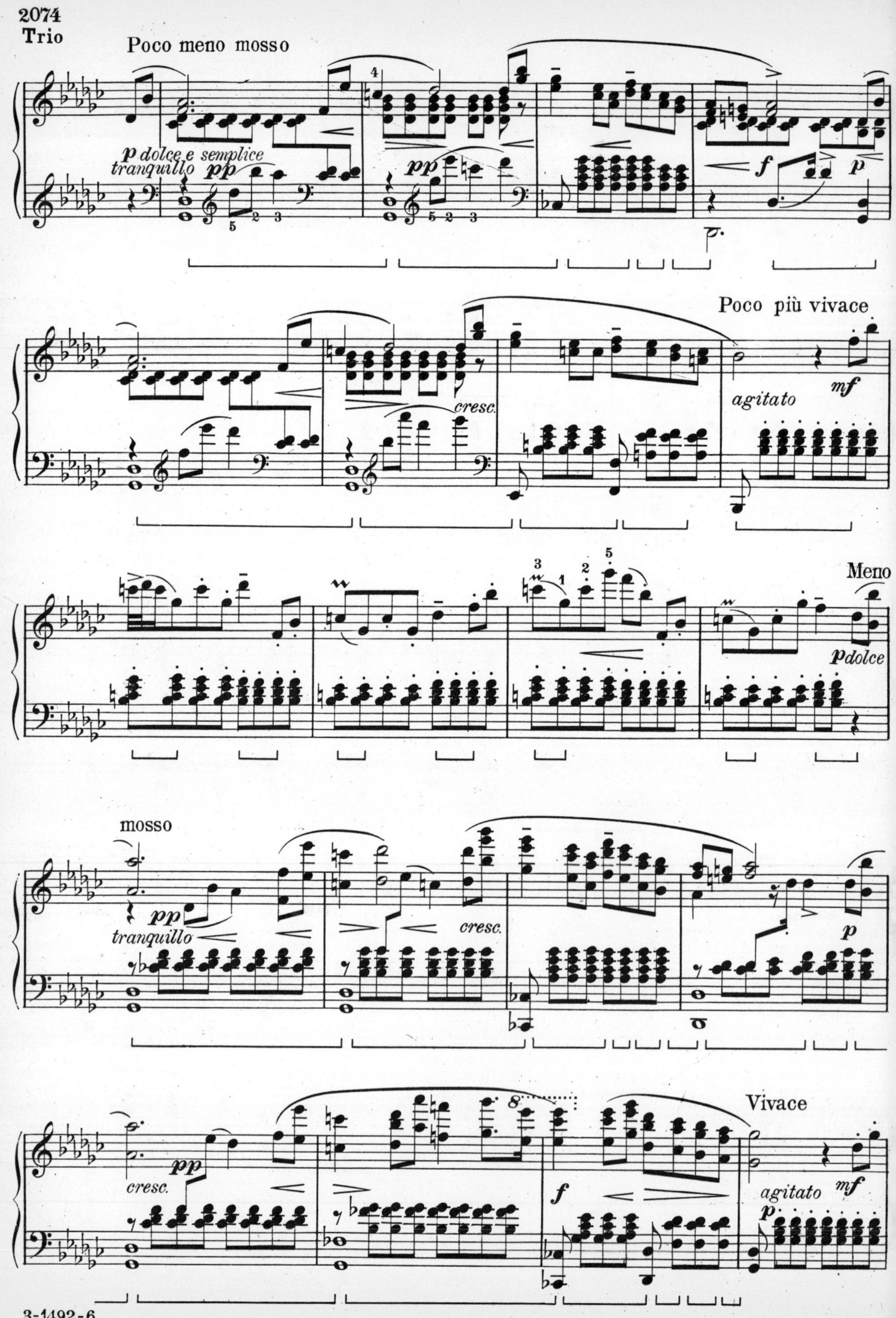
Poco meno mosso
p dolce e semplice
tranquillo
pp
pp
f
p
cresc.
Poco più vivace
agitato
mf
Meno
mosso
pdolce
pp
tranquillo
cresc.
p
cresc.
pp
f
Vivace
agitato
mf
p

pp
pp
pp
pp
pp
cresc. poco a poco
sempre staccato
f
marcato
cresc.
ff pesante
sostenuto
sf

Tempo I.

strepitoso
l. h.
sf
sf
Vivo
p
cresc.
f
cresc.
ff

BASSO OSTINATO

Edited by
Grover Brower

ANT. ARENSKY
Op. 5.

f
dim. e ritenuto
p
a tempo
p
Ped. *
p legatissimo
Ped.
simile
cresc.
f
dim.
mf
cresc.
f
cresc.

ritardando
cresc.
ff
cresc.
Meno mosso (grave)
fff
Ped.
simile
sempre fff
ritenuto
Tempo I.
p

mf
f
p
p
dim.
pp
pp
ritardando sempre
diminuendo
ppp
Ped.

CAPRICCIO
B MINOR

Edited by
A. Pero

JOHANNES BRAHMS,
Op. 76, No 2

Allegretto non troppo

Ped.
p
l.h.
sempre leggiero
p poco a poco più tranquillo

espress.
p
sempre dolce
l.h. sempre
dolce
l.h.
r.h.
Ped.
poco rit.

p a tempo

Ped. ❊ Ped. ❊

p *p* *cresc.*

Ped. ❊ Ped. ❊

sf l.h. *sf* l.h. *sf* l.h.

Ped. ❊ Ped. ❊ Ped. ❊

dim. senza rit.

p leggiero
Ped.
p
sempre p
l.h.

dim. sempre
Ped.
sempre più p
p rit. e dim.
una corda

PRÈS DE LA MER
BY THE SEA
Nº V, IN E-MINOR

Edited by
Nicholas de Vore

A. ARENSKY
Op. 52, Nº 5

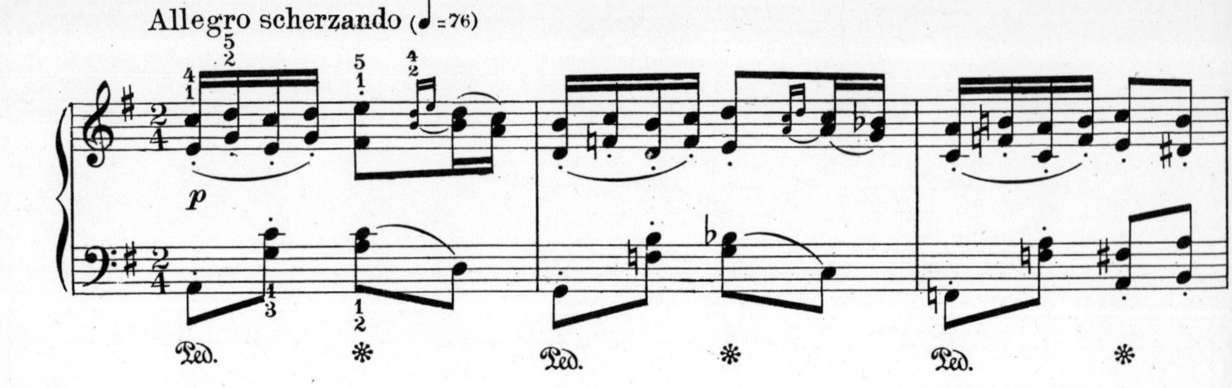

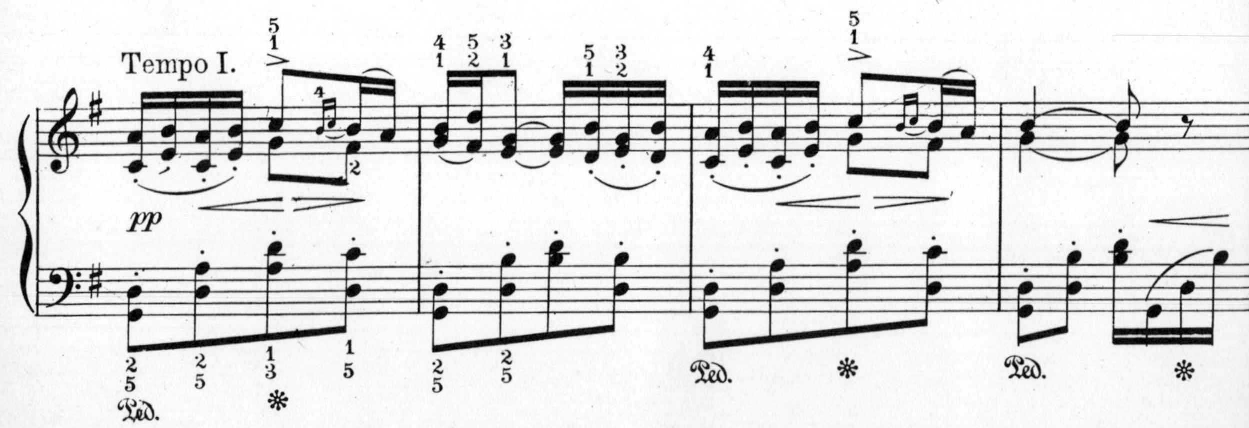

Poco meno mosso
mf
Tempo I.
pp
Ped.
Poco meno mosso
f
ritard.
mf
Tempo I
p
mf
p
ritard.

Allegretto sostenuto
mp a tempo
Ped.
mf
f
cresc.
Tempo I.
p
Ped.
Ped.
Ped.
mf
Poco meno mosso
p
a tempo
mp
poco ritenuto
cantabile

Tempo I.
pp
Poco meno mosso
mf
Tempo I.
pp
Poco meno mosso
ritard.
mf
Tempo I
p
mf
ritard.
pp

RÊVERIE

Edited by
A. Pero

CLAUDE DEBUSSY

Andante, senza rallentare (♩ = 108)

pp assai dolce ed espressivo

una corda

Ped. * Ped. * Ped. simile

p

mf

dim.

Ped. simile

p

poco rit.

pp a tempo

cresc. poco a poco

f
p
f
p
dim.
pp espressivo
mp
pp
sf
mf
p rit.
Ped.

p a tempo
più p
p
più p
pp
cresc.
mf
p
più p
pp
rit.

Tempo I.
p
Ped.
simile
ten.
p
Ped.
Ped.
Ped.
meno p
simile
p
p
rit.
p meno mosso
Ped.
più p
pp rall. e perdendosi
ppp
Ped.

NOCTURNE

F-SHARP MAJOR

From the CENTURY LIBRARY *of* MUSIC
Edited by Ignace J. Paderewski

CHOPIN
Op. 15, No. 2

dolciss.
p
fz
pp e poco riten.
con forza
a tempo
cresc.
string.
riten.
Doppio movimento-(ritmo)
sotto voce
a tempo
T.S.P.
cresc.
fz

cre - scen - do
decresc.
pfz
dim.
pp
molto rallent.
dim.
8va bassa ad lib.
smorz.
Tempo I.
dolce

leggierissimo
con forza
fz
r.h.
l.h.
tr
dim. rall.
pp
fz
a tempo
dim.
smorz.

PRELUDE

C MAJOR
J.S. BACH
PRELUDE
Allegro (♩ = 104)
p
cresc.
simile
f
p
f
p
f
U 214-5

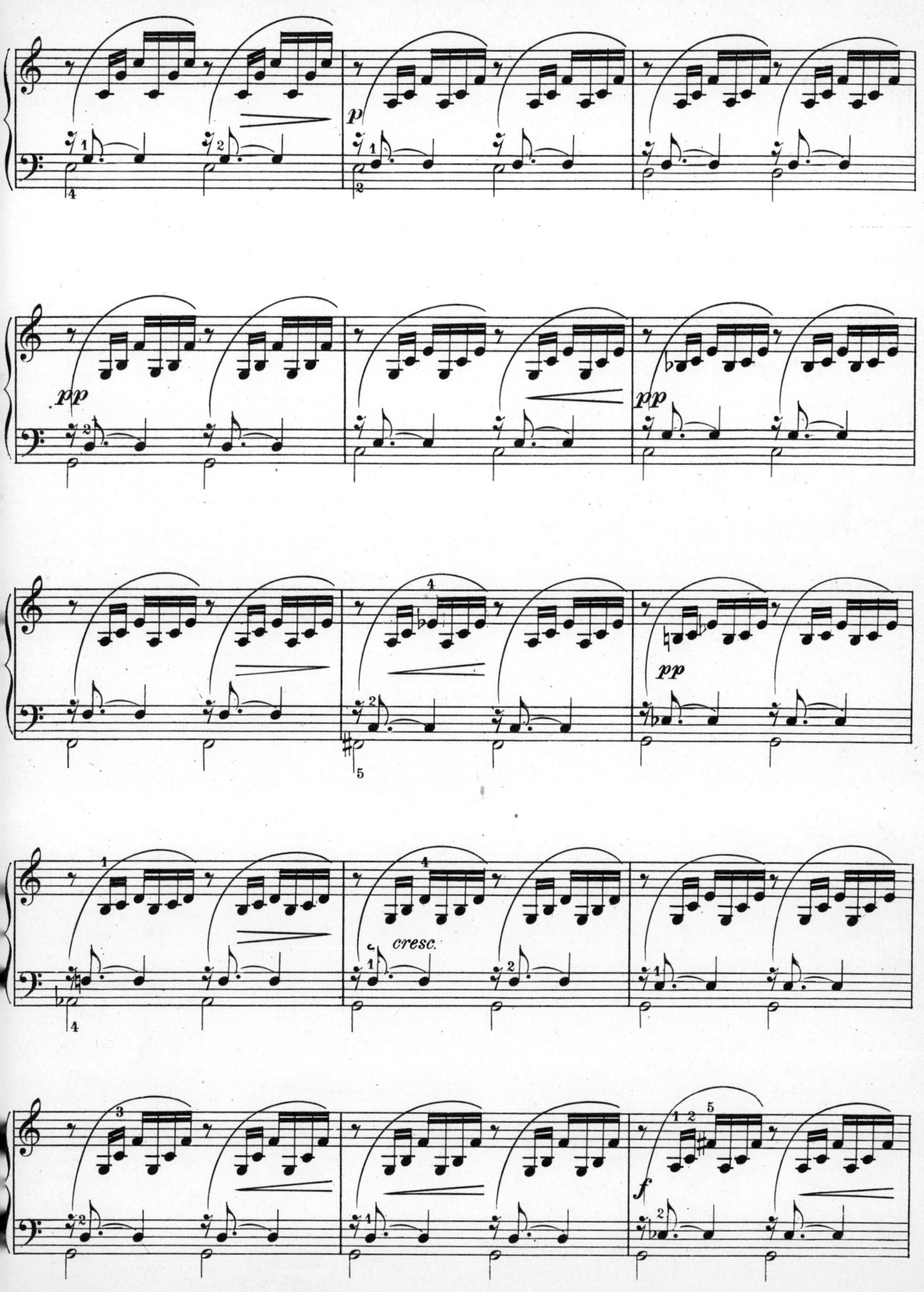
p
pp
pp
pp
cresc.
f

ff
mp
p
cantando
FUGUE (in 4 Voices)
Moderato (♩= 116)
p legatissimo
cresc.
f
p
cresc.

25
f
dim.
p
cresc.

dim.
p
l.h.
cresc.
f
dim.
p
rall. poco a poco
mp
p
pp

POLONAISE

C MINOR

From the CENTURY LIBRARY *of* MUSIC
Edited by Ignace J. Paderewski

Fr. CHOPIN
Op. 40, No. 2

dim.
f
Ped.
legato
cre -
- - - scen - - do
dim

ff
p
cresc.
dim
l.h.
l.h.

legato
cre - - scen - - do
dim.

sostenuto
p espress.
pp
f
ff
p

ff
p
dim.
slentando
p
pp
f
Ped.

cresc.
cre - - - scen - - - - do.
ff
Ped.
legato
Ped.
cre - - -
- scen -
- - - do
fff
Ped.

ARABESKE

Edited by
Charles Dennee

ROBERT SCHUMANN
Op. 18

Leggiero con tenerezza (♩ = 132)

a tempo
rit. poco a poco
a tempo
cresc.
sf
p
cresc.
sf
p
MINORE I
Poco meno mosso
mf

p
mf
f
cresc
ff

rit.
a tempo
rit.
a tempo
rit.
a tempo
rit.
a tempo
rit.
a tempo
rit.
a tempo
rit.
Tempo I
pp
cresc.
sf
p
cresc.
sf
p

p
rit. poco a poco
a tempo
Ped. come sopra
rit. poco a poco
a tempo
sf
p
sf
p

MINORE II

Poco meno mosso (♩ = 116)

f *p* *dim.*

rit. e dim.

f deciso a tempo

ff *sf* *sf*

f *p*

dim.

Ped. *

Tempo I.

rit. *pp* *sf* *p*

sf
p
p
rit. poco a poco
a tempo
rit. poco a poco
a tempo
sf
p

sf
p
rit.
CODA
Lento (𝅗𝅥 = 58)
espressivo molto
p
rit.
a tempo
rit.
f
r. h.
l. h.

ETUDE

C-MAJOR, № II.

Edited by
Charles Dennée

ANTON RUBINSTEIN
Op. 23, № 2.

f
p
f

p
sempre legato
p dolce.

p
8
p stacc.

p
p
8
8
8
8
3
3

p
cresc.
ritard.
a tempo.
ff

dim.
cresc.
8

8
p
8
8
pp
8
f
f

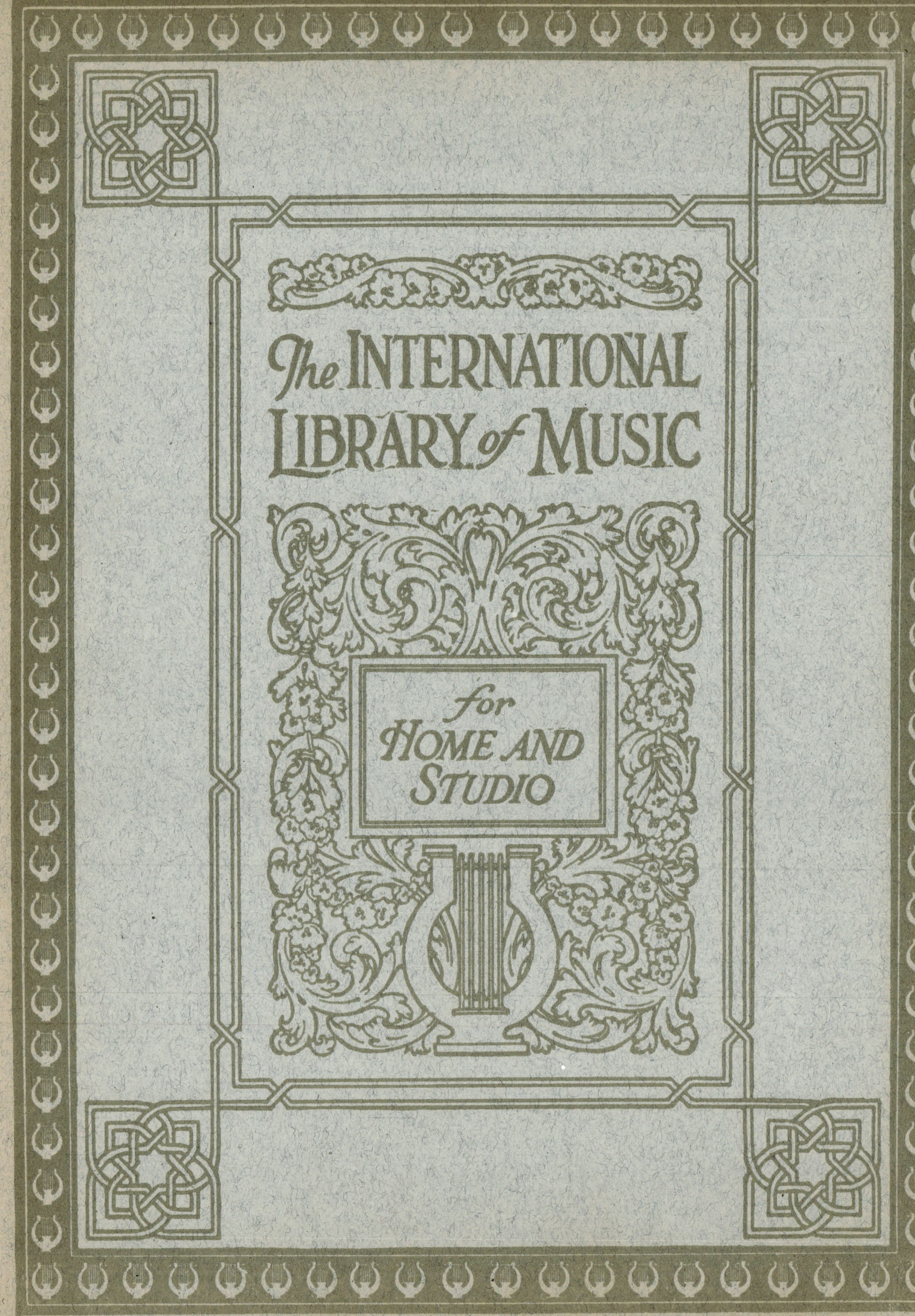
The INTERNATIONAL
LIBRARY of MUSIC
for
HOME AND
STUDIO